The following pages are for you to use in any way that you like. You may prefer a more formal layout, or many people are familiar with the beautiful chaos of a scrapbook style! Please do not feel you have to do anything in particular. This is your own, personal record of love and shared experiences.

Here are some ideas to help you.

• **Perhaps the first lined page could be used to record the official details.**

This could include birth and death dates, where and when remembrance gatherings are held (eg 2pm at St John's Church, led by Rev. Peter Smith), or details of the interment (eg Forest Lawn Cemetery, Plot 237).

• **The lined pages may be used to write names, contact details and messages.**

These pages could become a record of those that attend on the funeral day, or perhaps people could write in them at any time before or afterwards.

• **As a permanent record of Thankyou.**

It can be very useful to keep a record your correspondence at the emotional time of a funeral. Perhaps you would like to write down what others have done, and when you thanked them. This could include people who have sent flowers, or condolence cards and letters, or as a thank you for attending and other thoughtful actions.

• **The lined pages could easily be used for photographs.**

Once you have placed the photographs, the lines will provide a neat and easy way to write captions and other comments describing the photos.

• **Unlined pages are perfect for drawings, photographs and other creative ideas.**

Maybe you would like to stick in newspaper notices, or other treasured records of the funeral day. Children's drawings can be a wonderful memory as time goes by. Some families have even used this book to ink their own hand or thumbprints.

• **If you are preparing for your own funeral, perhaps make a start on the pages yourself!**

Like a photograph, audio recording, or video, permanent records of ourselves can become precious keepsakes in years to come. Sometimes known as an "emotional will", putting your thoughts and love down on paper can seem very difficult to start. But once you realize you don't have to be perfect (very few of our communications ever are!) you will hopefully enjoy the process. Just be you.

In Loving Memory of

Index

nos Recuerdos de
nuestro hermano
José

no seas tardona
la quedó

a Dios asta la
fin ya no la escribo

antes Abu
Recuerdos de
hermano

Poetry

There can be great comfort in
comfortable silence between friends,
but there can also come a time when
we yearn to share, to express, and to
put a voice to our innermost thoughts
and deepest feelings.

Perhaps there are no single words to
express our emotions, but when we put
groups of words together we can start to
open the door to our spirit and true self.

We may be bursting with wanting
to say something, but we just don't
know how to.

There is a way to move forward. While
we may struggle to find our own words,
we are still able to recognise what we
would like to say, when we read it from
the pen of others.

Following are some selections
from centuries of sacred and secular
(non-religious) writers. Some are entire
poems, some are excerpts from poems
or novels, and some are from sacred
texts or Divine inspiration.

Perhaps you are looking for a
reading to focus on the person that
has died, or perhaps you prefer a
reading that expresses your grief
that they have gone.

It can be very memorable, and healing,
to consider writing your own poem
or tribute to someone that has died.

"My One True Thing" is a excellent
example of poetry describing the
characteristics or cherished memories
of a loved one. It does not have to
rhyme, and writing in short groups
of words can condense our feelings
into a very powerful tribute.

Children need to express their feelings
too, and can often be a surprising
inspiration with their intuitive ability
to clearly say what really matters most.

We never walk alone, and it can be
a great comfort to take shelter in the
great wordsmiths and traditions that
have travelled this road before us.

I Am Not Alone

Claribel Alegria 1924 –
Nicaraguan Poet, translated by Carolyn Forché

I am not alone
and never will be

Your absence is my company

Farewell

Anne Bronte 1820 – 1849
English Poet, from family of literary women

Farewell to Thee! But not farewell
To all my fondest thoughts of Thee;

Within my heart they still shall dwell
And they shall cheer and comfort me.

Life seems more sweet that Thou didst live
And men more true that Thou wert one;

Nothing is lost that Thou didst give,
Nothing destroyed that Thou hast done.

Miss Me, But Let Me Go

Unknown

When I come to the end of the road
And the sun has set for me,

I want no rites in a gloom-filled room
Why cry for a soul set free?

Miss me a little – but not too long
And not with your head bowed low.

Remember the love that once was shared
Miss me, but let me go.

For this is a journey we all must take
And each must go alone.

It's all part of the master's plan,
A step on the road to home.

When you are lonely and sick of heart,
Go to the friends we know.

Bear your sorrow in good deeds.
Miss me, but let me go.

A Song of Living

Amelia Josephine Burr 1878 – 1968
American Poet

Because I have loved life,
I shall have no sorrow to die.

I have sent up my gladness on wings, to be lost in the blue of the sky.

I have run and leaped with the rain,
I have taken the wind to my breast.

My cheek like a drowsy child to the face of the earth I have pressed.

Because I have loved life, I shall have no sorrow to die.

I have kissed young Love on the lips,
I have heard his song to the end.

I have struck my hand like a seal in the loyal hand of a friend.

I have known the peace of heaven,
the comfort of work done well.

I have longed for death in the darkness and risen alive out of hell.

Because I have loved life, I shall have no sorrow to die.

My One True Thing

Lyn Anderson 1945 –
Australian Poet

My one true thing
I woke, you'd gone
Chance to speak
Gone forever

Plans to share memories of Home
Memories of abundance in hard times
Overflowing garden
Wild daisies flowing with the wind

Deep perfumed dark roses, stocks and carnations
Forever flowering succulents long before the fashion
Ripe mulberry, orange, lemons, peach and fig trees
Jam making sealed with hot glue

Constant warmth from a wood stove
Smell of a roast in the oven
Bread and butter pudding, the best I'll ever taste
Fruit salad and cream

Singing old fashioned songs
With old fashioned meanings
I could write a sonnet about your Easter bonnet...
You always hurt the one you love...

Lazy nights on a cool lawn
Millions of stars in a warm black sky
Talking of Robert Askin's politics
Dreaming of the best holiday and fishing spots on the coast

White sheets flapping with the wind
Stiff white tablecloths, folded napkins
Polished silverware
Flowers everywhere

Busy people, your home, my memories
My beautiful mother who never asked much from life
Yet gave so much to so many people
My one true friend, my centre, you're gone

Thank you for a gentle life with honest people
You warned me many times, I had no courage to see
You would say that's ok
But I want to talk to you today

I travel another road, one day at a time
Your memory my guide
You're with Dad, Thelma, Clem, Nana, Granddad and Jim
It's the way of things

Nourished by your generous gardens
Pouring onto pathways, climbing the cracks
Your generous kitchen nourishing all
I have one who is starving

I know you would help me if you could
But rest well my mother
Your work is done
I will carry on

Traditional Gaelic Blessing

May the road rise up to meet you.
May the wind be always at your back.

May the sun shine warm upon your face;
the rains fall soft upon your fields

And until we meet again,
may God hold you in the palm of His hand.

Eternity

William Blake 1757 – 1827
English Artist, Engraver, Mystic and Poet

He who binds to himself a joy
Does the winged life destroy;

But he who kisses the joy as it flies
Lives in eternity's sun rise.

The Hands of Time

Unknown

The clock of life is wound but once
No-one has the power

to tell just when the hands may stop
The year, the day, the hour

When you plan a kindly deed
Act now, use all your skill

The present only is our own.
Live, love, toil with a will.

Wait not until tomorrow
The hands may then be still

Remember

Christina Rossetti 1830 – 1894
English Poet

Remember me when I am gone away,
Gone far away into the silent land;

When you can no more hold me by the hand,
Nor I half turn to go, yet turning stay.

Remember me when no more day by day
You tell me of our future that you planned

Only remember me; you understand
It will be late to counsel then or pray

Yet if you should forget me for a while
And afterwards remember, do not grieve:

For if the darkness and corruption leave
A vestige of the thoughts that once I had,

Better by far you should forget and smile
Than that you should remember and be sad.

Poem

James Langston Hughes 1902 – 1967
American Author, Playwright and Poet

I loved my friend.
He went away from me.
There's nothing more to say.

The poem ends, Soft as it began –
I loved my friend

Even Such is Time

Sir Walter Raleigh 1552 – 1618
English Navigator, Historian and Poet

Even such is time, which takes in trust
Our youth, our joys, and all we have,
And pays us but with age and dust;

Who, in the dark and silent grave,
When we have wandered all our ways,
Shuts up the story of our days,

And from which earth and grave and dust,
The Lord shall rise me up, I trust.

So What is Love?

Unknown

So what is love? If thou wouldst know
The heart alone can tell:

Two minds with but a single thought,
Two hearts that beat as one.

And whence comes Love? Like morning bright
Love comes without thy call.

And how dies Love? A spirit bright,
Love never dies at all.

I'd Like

Unknown

I'd like the memory of me to be a happy one.
I'd like to leave an afterglow of smiles when life is done.

I'd like to leave an echo whispering softly down the ways,
of happy times, laughing times and bright and sunny days.

I'd like the tears of those who grieve,
to dry before the sun of happy memories that I leave,
when life is done.

A Ship Sails

From "Toilers of the Sea"
Victor Hugo 1862 – 1926
French Author, exiled to Guernsey

I am standing upon that foreshore.
A ship at my side spreads her white sails in the morning breeze
and starts for the blue ocean.

She is an object of beauty and strength
and I stand and watch her
until at length she hangs like a speck of white cloud
just where the sea and sky come down to mingle with each other.

Then someone at my side says:
"There! She is gone!"

"Gone where?"

"Gone from my sight, that is all."

She is just as large in mast and spar and hull
As ever she was when she left my side;
just as able to bear her load of living freight to the place of her destination.

Her diminished size is in me, not in her.

And just at that moment, when someone at my side says
"There! She is gone!"
there are other eyes watching her coming
and other voices ready to take up the glad shout –

"Here she comes!"

You'll Never Walk Alone

From "Carousel"
Oscar Hammerstein 11 1895 – 1960
American Writer and Musical Director

When you walk through the storm
Hold your head up high,
And don't be afraid of the dark

At the end of the storm
is a golden sky
And the sweet silver song of a lark.

Walk on through the wind,
Walk on through the rain,
Though your dreams be tossed and blown

Walk on, walk on,
With hope in your heart
And you'll never walk alone

You'll never walk alone.

Not How Did He Die

Unknown

Not how did he die, but how did he live?

Not what did he gain, but what did he give?

These are the units to measure the worth
Of a man as a man, regardless of birth.

Not what was his church, or what was his creed,
But had he befriended those really in need?

Not what was his station, but had he a heart?
How did he play in his God-given part?

Was he ever ready, with words of good cheer,
To bring back a smile, to banish a tear?

Not how did the formal obituary run,

But how many grieved when his life's work was done?

Perhaps

Nellie Smith 1939 –
English Poet

Perhaps the truth will be

That we on Earth are actually at school
Still working hard to live and love and learn

And those who have lived a physical life

Will finally pass on to reunite
With everybody else, now relaxing at home

Cheerful and safe

Joy in Death

Emily Dickinson 1830 – 1886
American Poet

If tolling bell I ask the cause.

'A soul has gone to God,'
I'm answered in a lonesome tone;

Is heaven then so sad?

The bells should joyful ring to tell
A soul had gone to heaven,
Would seem to me the proper way
A good news should be given.

Memory

Unknown

They say memories are golden
well maybe that is true.
But I never wanted memories,
I only wanted you.

So many times I've needed you,
So many times I've cried.
If love alone could save you
you never would have died.

In life I loved you dearly,
In death I love you still.
In my heart you hold a place
no one else will ever fill.

If tears could build a stairway
and heartache make a lane,
I'd walk the path to heaven
and bring you back again.

Even though your time is over
and I must walk alone
My smile stays with our memories
My heart is your new home

Up-Hill

Christina Rossetti 1830 – 1894
English Poet

Does the road wind up-hill all the way?
Yes, to the very end.

Will the day's journey take the whole long day?
From morn to night, my friend.

But is there for the night a resting-place?
A roof for when the slow dark hours begin.

May not the darkness hide it from my face?
You cannot miss that inn.

Shall I meet other wayfarers at night?
Those who have gone before.

Then must I knock, or call when just in sight?
They will not keep you standing at that door.

Shall I find comfort, travel-sore and weak?
Of labour you shall find the sum.

Will there be beds for me and all who seek?
Yea, beds for all who come.

Desiderata

Max Ehrmann 1872 – 1945
American Lawyer and Poet

Go placidly amid the noise and haste,
and remember what peace there may be in silence.

As far as possible, without surrender,
be on good terms with all persons.

Speak your truth quietly and clearly; and listen to others,
even to the dull and ignorant; they too have their story.
Avoid loud and aggressive persons, they are vexations to the spirit.

If you compare yourself to others, you may become vain and bitter,
for always there will be greater and lesser persons than yourself.
Enjoy your achievements as well as your plans.

Keep interested in your own career, however humble;
it is a real possession in the changing fortunes of time.
Exercise caution in your business affairs, for the world is full of trickery.

But let this not blind you to what virtue there is;
Many persons strive for high ideals,
and everywhere life is full of heroism.

Be yourself.
Especially do not feign affection.
Neither be cynical about love;
for in the face of all aridity and disenchantment
it is as perennial as the grass.

Take kindly the counsel of the years,
gracefully surrendering the things of youth.

Nurture strength of spirit to shield you in sudden misfortune.
But do not distress yourself with dark imaginings.
Many fears are born of fatigue and loneliness.

Beyond a wholesome discipline, be gentle with yourself.
You are a child of the universe no less than the trees and the stars;
you have a right to be here.

And whether or not it is clear to you,
no doubt the universe is unfolding as it should.

Therefore be at peace with God,
whatever you conceive Him to be.

And whatever your labours and aspirations,
in the noisy confusion of life,
keep peace with your soul.

With all its sham, drudgery and broken dreams,
it is still a beautiful world.

Be cheerful.
Strive to be happy.

Funeral Blues

W.H. Auden 1907 – 1973
English born American Poet

Stop all the clocks, cut off the telephone,
Prevent the dog from barking with a juicy bone,

Silence the pianos and with muffled drum
Bring out the coffin, let the mourners come.

Let aeroplanes circle moaning overhead
Scribbling on the sky the message He Is Dead,

Put the crepe bows round the necks of the public doves,
Let the traffic policemen wear black cotton gloves.

He was my North, my South, my East and West,
My working week and my Sunday rest,

My noon, my midnight, my talk, my song;
I thought that love would last forever: I was wrong.

The stars are not wanted now: put out every one;
Pack up the moon and dismantle the sun;

Pour away the ocean and sweep up the wood.
For nothing now can ever come to any good.

When We Remember

Unknown

You can shed tears that she is gone
or you can smile because she has lived.

You can close your eyes and pray that she'll come back
or you can open your eyes and see all she's left.

Your heart can be empty because you can't see her
or you can be full of the love you shared.

You can turn your back on tomorrow and live yesterday
or you can be happy for tomorrow because of yesterday.

You can remember her and only that she's gone
or you can cherish her memory and let it live on.

You can cry and close your mind, be empty and turn your back
or you can do what she'd want:
smile,
open your eyes,
love
and go on.

On Death

Kahlil Gibran 1883 – 1931
Lebanese Poet and Artist, died USA

You would know the secret of death.
But how shall you find it unless you seek it in the heart of life?

The owl whose night-bound eyes are blind unto the day
cannot unveil the mystery of light.
If you would indeed behold the spirit of death,
open your heart wide unto the body of life.

For life and death are one,
even as the river and the sea are one.
In the depth of your hopes and desires
lies your silent knowledge of the beyond;

And like seeds dreaming beneath the snow
your heart dreams of spring.
Trust the dreams,
for in them is hidden the gate to eternity.

For what is it to die
but to stand naked in the wind and to melt into the sun?
And what is it to cease breathing,
but to free the breath from its restless tides,
that it may rise and expand and seek God unencumbered?

Only when you drink from the river of silence shall you indeed sing.
And when you have reached the mountain top,
then you shall begin to climb.
And when the earth shall claim your limbs,
then shall you truly dance.

Indian Prayer

Traditional

When I am dead
Cry for me a little
Think of me sometimes

But not too much.

Think of me now and again
As I was in life
At some moments it's pleasant to recall

But not for long.

Leave me in peace
And I shall leave you in peace

And while you live,
Let your thoughts be with the living.

Do Not Stand at My Grave and Weep

Mary Frye 1905 – 2004
American Housewife and Poet

Do not stand at my grave and weep,
I am not there, I do not sleep.

I am a thousand winds that blow,
I am the diamond glints on snow,

I am the sunlight and ripened grain.
I am the gentle Autumn rain.

When you awake in the morning hush,
I am the swift upflinging rush

Of quiet birds in circling flight.
I am the soft star shine at night.

Do not stand at my grave and cry,
I am not there, I did not die.

To My Dear and Loving Husband

Anne Bradstreet 1612 – 1672
American Puritan Poet, born in England

If ever two were one then surely we.
If ever man were loved by wife, then thee;

If ever wife were happy in a man,
Compare with me, ye women, if you can.

I prize thy love more than whole mines of gold
Or all the riches that the East doth hold.

My love is such that rivers cannot quench,
Nor aught but love from thee give recompense.

Thy love is such I can no way repay,
The heavens reward thee manifold, I pray.

Then while we live, in love let's so persevere
That when we live no more, we may live ever.

Do Not Go Gentle into That Good Night

Dylan Thomas 1914 – 1953
Welsh Poet

Do not go gentle into that good night,
Old age should burn and rave at close of day;
Rage, rage against the dying of the light.

Though wise men at their end know dark is right,
Because their words had forked no lightning they
Do not go gentle into that good night.

Good men, the last wave by, crying how bright
Their frail deeds might have danced in a green bay,
Rage, rage against the dying of the light.

Wild men who caught and sang the sun in flight,
And learn, too late, they grieved it on its way,
Do not go gentle into that good night.

Grave men, near death, who see with blinding sight
Blind eyes could blaze like meteors and be gay,
Rage, rage against the dying of the light.

And you, my father, there on the sad height,
Curse, bless, me now with your fierce tears, I pray.
Do not go gentle into that good night.
Rage, rage against the dying of the light.

Lighthouse

Joanne Douglass 1961 –
New Zealand Widow

There may be times ahead
when I question
the reason you are gone
and how I might now fashion my future

There may be times ahead
that leave me without a shell
to protect and defend my uncertain position
in the face of new challenges

There may be times ahead
when I question
the purpose and form
of this confusing, frustrating existence

But there will never, ever be a time
when I wonder if I was loved.

I Have Something to Say

Joanne Smith 1927 –
Australian Poet

As I grow older, the possibility of my funeral becomes more likely.

Like some child's joke, told too often, the painful humour
quickly becomes obvious, and then inevitable.

So on this appointed day
If I might be somehow present (always a possibility)
What do I hope to look upon?

Listen closely.
Because when my loved ones gather
I am certain of what I would like for them.

Peace.

Not the peace that comes after long wringing of emotion,
Of painful questions and confusion
And desperate blocking to prevent falling into the abyss

No way! The peace I hope to look upon
Will be active, and full, and honest.

Like that glorious moment just before sleep,
Floating into bed at the end of a magnificent party
Exhausted and nourished by the certainty of friends
The richness of shared experience,
and of love.

Starfish

Unknown

A child walked along the beach,
stopping every few steps to pick up a starfish.

There were hundreds scattered near the crashing waves.
All thrown up by the latest storm, and abandoned on the sand
to the growing heat of the day.

Fascinated, I watched her zig-zag path.
She would quickly examine each one,
then gently float it away on the receding tide,
back to the safety of their ocean home.

Touched by her efforts, I said
"There are far too many to rescue, how can you possibly
hope to make a difference?"

She looked thoughtfully at the starfish in her hand,
then placed it back in the water.

Smiling, she turned her eyes to meet mine.
"I made a difference to that one."

If I Should Go

Unknown

If I should go tomorrow
It would never be goodbye,
For I have left my heart with you,
So don't you ever cry.

The love that's deep within me,
Shall reach you from the stars,
You'll feel it from the heavens,
And it will heal the scars.

I Have Seen Death Too Often

Unknown

I have seen death too often
To believe in death:

For it is like arriving at the end of the day,
Turning off the engine, switching off the lights,
And gently closing the car door;

Then walking up the path, up to the steps
And into the light of home.

Young Life Cut Short –
For the Brother of My Friend

Unknown

Do not judge a biography by its length,
Nor by the number of pages in it.

Judge it by the richness of it's contents

Sometimes those unfinished are among the most poignant…

Do not judge a song by its duration
Nor by the number of its notes

Judge it by the way it touches and lifts the soul

Sometimes those unfinished are among the most beautiful…

And when something has enriched your life
And when it's melody lingers on in your heart

Is it unfinished?

Or is it endless?

I'll Be There

Maude Hurford
Guernsey Poet

I've come to the end of life's busy road
I've put down my burden, I've cast off my load

My spirit is free, my soul has wings
I'll pour from the throat of a bird that sings

I'll ride on the wind, I'll float on the clouds
I'll twinkle with the stars in night's velvet shroud

I'll shine with the sun as it circles the earth
I'll be there at the dawn when a new day gives birth

I'll be with the snow fluttering down
Silently, softly, nature's crown

I'll be in the rain as it falls on the earth
Cleansing, refreshing, priceless worth

I'll ride on the ether, silent and free
A world of my own, please don't cry for me

Come To Me

Unknown

God saw you getting tired
and a cure was not to be
so he put his arms around you
and whispered,
"Come to Me"

With tearful eyes we watch you
and saw you pass away
and although we loved you dearly
we could not make you stay.

A Golden heart stopped beating
hard working hands at rest.
God broke our hearts to prove us
he only takes the best

Break, Break, Break

Lord Alfred Tennyson 1809 – 1892
English Royal Poet Laureate for 40 years

Break, break, break
On thy cold grey stones, O Sea!
And I would that my tongue could utter
The thoughts that arise in me.

O well for the fisherman's boy,
That he shouts with his sister at play!
O well for the sailor lad,
That he sings in his boat on the bay!

And the stately ships go on
To their haven under the hill;
But O for the touch of a vanish'd hand,
And the sound of a voice that is still!

Break, break, break
At the foot of the crags, O Sea!
But the tender grace of a day that is dead
Will never come back to me.

When You Are Old

W.B. Yeats 1865 – 1939
Irish Dramatist and Poet

When you are old and grey and full of sleep,
And nodding by the fire, take down this book,

And slowly read, and dream of the soft look
Your eyes had once, and of their shadows deep;

How many loved your moments of glad grace,
And loved your beauty with love false or true,

But one man loved the pilgrim soul in you,
And loved the sorrows of your changing face;

And bending down beside the glowing bars,
Murmur, a little sadly, how Love fled

And paced upon the mountains overhead
And hid his face amid a crowd of stars.

From "Little Women"

Louisa May Alcott 1832 – 1888
American Novelist

Beth could not reason upon
or explain the faith
that gave her courage and patience to give up life,
and cheerfully wait for death.

Like a confiding child, she asked no questions,
but left everything to God and nature,
Father and Mother of us all,
feeling sure that they, and they only,
could teach and strengthen heart and spirit for this life
and the life to come.

To All Parents

Edgar Guest 1881 – 1959
American Poet

"I'll lend you for a little time a child of mine," He said.
"For you to love the while he lives and mourn when he is dead,

"It may be six or seven years, or twenty-two or three,
"But will you, till I call him back, take care of him for me?

"He'll bring his charms to gladden you, but should his stay be brief,
"You'll have his lovely memories, as solace for your grief,

"I cannot promise he will stay, since all from earth return,
"But there are lessons taught down there I want this child to learn.

"I've looked the wide world over in my search for teachers true,
"And from the throngs that crowd life's lanes I have selected you.

"Now will you give him all your love, nor think the labor vain,
"Nor hate me when I come to call to take him back again?

I fancied that I heard them say: "Dear Lord, Thy will be done!
"For all the joy Thy child shall bring, the risk of grief we'll run.

We'll shelter him with tenderness; we'll love him while we may,
And for happiness we've known forever grateful stay.

"But should the angels call for him much sooner than we'd planned,
"We'll brave the bitter grief that comes and try to understand."

My Love

Claribel Alegria 1924 –
Nicaraguan Poet, translated by Carolyn Forché

Give me your hand my love
don't let me sink into sadness.

My body has already learned
the grief of your absence
but despite the blows
it still wants to live.

Don't go away
love
meet me in my dreams
defend your memory
my memory of you
that I don't want to lose.

We are voice and echo
mirror and face
give me your hand

Wait
I have to rearrange my time
until I reach you

Death, Where Is Thy Sting?

From "The Pilgrim's Progress"
John Bunyan 1628 – 1688
English Preacher and Writer

Then said he, "I am going to my Father's,
and though with great difficulty I am going hither,
yet now I do not repent me of all the trouble I have been at,
to arrive where I am.

My sword I give to him that shall succeed me in my pilgrimage,
and my courage and skill to him that can get it.

My marks and scars I carry with me, to be a witness for me,
that I have fought His battles, who now will be my rewarder."

When the day that he must go hence was come,
many accompanied him to the riverside,
into which as he went he said
"Death, where is thy sting?"

And as he went down deeper, he said
"Grave, where is thy victory?"

So, he passed over,
and all the trumpets sounded for him on the other side.

Crossing the Bar

Lord Alfred Tennyson 1809 – 1892
English Royal Poet Laureate for 40 years

Sunset and evening star,
And one clear call for me!
And may there be no moaning of the bar,
When I put out to sea,

But such a tide as moving seems asleep,
Too full for sound and foam,
When that which drew from out the boundless deep
Turns again home.

Twilight and evening bell,
And after that the dark!
And may there be no sadness of farewell,
When I embark;

For tho' from out our bourne of Time and Place
The flood may bear me far,
I hope to see my Pilot face to face
When I have crost the bar.

Footprints

Unknown

One night a man had a dream.

He dreamed he was walking along the beach with the Lord.
Across the sky flashed scenes from his life.

When the last scene had played,
he looked back at the footprints in the sand.
He noticed that many times along the path of life
there were only one set of footprints.

He also noticed that it happened at the very lowest
and saddest times in his life.
This really bothered him and he questioned the Lord about it.

"Lord, you said that once I decided to follow you,
you'd walk with me all the way.
But I have noticed that during the most troublesome times in my life,
there is only one set of footprints.
I don't understand why when I needed you most you would leave me."

The Lord replied,
"My son, My precious child,
I love you and would never leave you.
During your times of trial and suffering,
When you see only one set of footprints,
it was then that
I carried you."

Epitaph on William Muir

Robert Burns 1759 – 1796
Scottish Poet

An honest man here lies at rest,
As e'er God with His image blest:

The friend of man, the friend of truth,
The friend of age, the guide of youth:

Few hearts like his – with virtue warm'd,
Few heads with knowledge so inform'd:

If there's another world, he lives in bliss;
If there is none, he made the best of this.

From a Gravestone in Sutcombe, Devon

The lovely bud, so young, so fair
Called off by earthly doom,
Just came to show how sweet a flower
In paradise could bloom

Death Cannot Kill What Never Dies

From "Fruits of Solitude" Part II Union of Friends
William Penn 1644 – 1718
Quaker Theologist and Founder of Pennsylvania

They that love beyond the world cannot be separated by it.
Death cannot kill what never dies.

Nor can spirits ever be divided
That love and live in the same divine principle:
the root and record of their friendship.

Death is but a crossing the world as friends do seas;
they live in one another still.

For they must needs be present
that love and live in that which is omnipresent.

In this Divine glass they see face to face;
and their converse is free as well as pure.

This is the comfort of friends,
that though they may be said to die,
yet their friendship and society are, in the best sense,
ever present,
because immortal.

Speak to Us of Joy and Sorrow

Kahlil Gibran 1883 – 1931
Lebanese Poet and Artist, died USA

Then a woman said, "Speak to us of Joy and Sorrow."
And He answered:

"Your joy is your sorrow unmasked.
And the selfsame well from which your laughter rises was oftentimes
filled with your tears.

And how else can it be?

The deeper your sorrow carves into your being,
the more joy you can contain.

Is not the cup that holds your wine
the very cup that was burned in the potter's oven?

And is not the lute that soothes your spirit
the very wood that was hollowed by knives?

When you are joyous,
look deep into your heart and you shall find
it is only that which has given you sorrow
that is giving you joy."

All Is Well

Henry Scott Holland 1847 – 1918
Canon of St Paul's Cathedral, London

Death is nothing at all,
I have only slipped into the next room

I am I and you are you
Whatever we were to each other, that we are still.

Call me by my old familiar name,
Speak to me in the easy way which you always used
Put no difference in your tone,
Wear no forced air of solemnity or sorrow

Laugh as we always laughed at the little jokes we enjoyed together.
Play, smile, think of me, pray for me.

Let my name be ever the household world that it always was,
Let it be spoken without effect, without the trace of shadow on it.

Life means all that it ever meant.
It is the same as it ever was, there is unbroken continuity.

Why should I be out of mind because I am out of sight?

I am waiting for you, for an interval, somewhere very near,
Just around the corner.

All is well.

'Tis Better to Have Loved

Lord Alfred Tennyson 1809 – 1892
English Royal Poet Laureate for 40 years

I envy not in any moods
the captive void of noble rage,
the linnet born within the cage
that never knew the summer woods:

I envy not the beast that takes
his license in the field of time,
unfetter'd by the sense of crime,
to whom a conscience never wakes;

Nor, what may count itself as blest,
the heart that never plighted troth
but stagnates in the weeds of sloth,
nor any want-begotten rest.

I hold it true, whate'er befall;
I feel it when I sorrow most;
'Tis better to have loved and lost
Than never to have loved at all.

When I Am Gone

Unknown

When I am gone release me,
Let me go, I have so many things to see and do.

You mustn't tie yourself to me with tears,
Be happy that we had so many beautiful years

I gave to you my love.
You can only guess how much you gave me in happiness.

I thank you for the love you each have shown,
But now it's time I travel alone.

So grieve for me a while, if you must
Then let your grief be comforted by my trust.

It's only for a while we must part,
So bless the memories in your heart.

I won't be far away, for life carries on,
So if you need me, call and I will come.

Though you can't see or touch me, I'll be near.
And if you listen within your heart you'll hear

All my love around you soft and clear.
And then when you must come this way alone

I'll greet you with a smile and say
"Welcome Home"

Divine Love Cannot Change

From "War and Peace"
Leo Tolstoy 1828 – 1910
Russian Novelist and Activist

Loving with human love,
one may pass from love to hatred;
but divine love cannot change.

Nothing, not even death, can shatter it.
It is the very nature of the soul...
Love is life.

All, all that I understand,
I understand only because I love.

All is bound up in love alone.
Love is God,
and dying means for me a particle of love,
to go back to the universal and eternal source of love.

I Am Making All Things New

From the CHRISTIAN BIBLE
Revelation 21:1-7

I, John, saw a new heaven and a new earth;
for the first heaven and the first earth had passed away,
and the sea was no more.

And I saw the holy city, the new Jerusalem,
coming down out of heaven from God,
prepared as a bride adorned for her husband.
And I heard a loud voice from the throne saying,

'See, the home of God is among mortals.
He will dwell with them;
they will be his peoples,
and God himself will be with them;
he will wipe every tear from their eyes.
Death will be no more;
mourning and crying and pain will be no more,
for the first things have passed away.'

And the one who was seated on the throne said,
'See, I am making all things new.'

Also he said,
'Write this, for these words are trustworthy and true.'
Then he said to me,
'It is done!
I am the Alpha and the Omega, the beginning and the end.
To the thirsty I will give water as a gift from the spring of the water of life.
Those who conquer will inherit these things,
and I will be their God and they will be my children.'

A Time For All Things

From the CHRISTIAN BIBLE
Ecclesiastes 3:1-8

For everything there is a season,
And a time for every matter under heaven:

A time to be born, and a time to die;
A time to plant, and a time to pluck up what is planted;
A time to kill, and a time to heal;

A time to break down, and a time to build up;
A time to weep, and a time to laugh;

A time to mourn, and a time to dance;
A time to throw away stones, and a time to gather stones together;

A time to embrace, And a time to refrain from embracing;
A time to seek, and a time to lose;

A time to keep, and a time to throw away;
A time to tear, and a time to sew;

A time to keep silence, and a time to speak;
A time to love, and a time to hate,

A time for war, and a time for peace.

The Lord is My Shepherd

From the CHRISTIAN BIBLE
Psalm 23

The Lord is my shepherd, I shall not want.

He makes me lie down in green pastures,
He leads me beside quiet waters,
He restores my soul.
He guides me in paths of righteousness for His name's sake.

Even though I walk through the valley of the shadow of death,
I will fear no evil, for you are with me;
Your rod and your staff, they comfort me.

You prepare a table before me in the presence of my enemies.
You anoint my head with oil; my cup overflows.

Surely goodness and love will follow me all the days of my life,
And I will dwell in the house of the Lord forever.

Lord, We Turn to You

From the JEWISH FUNERAL SERVICE PRAYER BOOK

Lord, we turn to you in our grief and bewilderment,
for a mystery surrounds the birth and death of man.

Your will summons us into this world and then calls us to depart,
but Your plan is so vast and Your purposes so deep
that our understanding fails, and our reason cannot follow.

Yet You have taught us that time and space are not the measure
of all things.
Beyond them is the life of eternity.
We do not die into the grave but into the love of God.

It has been Your will to receive the soul of him/her,
to bring him/her to the life everlasting,
and she/he is beyond the tragedies of this world.

We shall find our comfort in Your teaching.
Beyond the grave we shall meet together
in the life that has no end.

The Greatest of These is Love

From the CHRISTIAN BIBLE
Corinthians 1:13

If I speak in the tongues of men and of angels,
but have not love,
I am a noisy gong or a clanging cymbal.

And if I have the prophetic powers,
and understand all mysteries and all knowledge,
and if I have all faith, so as to remove mountains,
but have not love,
I am nothing.

If I give away all I have,
and if I deliver my body to be burned,
but have not love,
I gain nothing.

Love is patient, love is kind;
Love is not jealous, or boastful; it is not arrogant or rude.
Love does not insist on its own way;
it is not irritable or resentful;
it does not rejoice at wrong, but rejoices in right.

Love bears all things, believes all things,
hopes all things, endures all things.

Love never ends;
As for prophesies, they will pass away
As for tongues, they will cease
As for knowledge, it will pass away.
For our knowledge is imperfect and our prophecy is imperfect;
But when the perfect comes, the imperfect will pass away.
When I was a child,
I spoke like a child, I thought like a child, I reasoned like a child;
When I became a man,
I gave up the childish ways.

For now we see in a mirror dimly,
but then face-to-face.

Now I know in part;
then I shall understand fully,
even as I have been fully understood.

There are three things that last forever –
Faith
Hope and
Love

But the greatest of these is love.

Look to This Day!

From the SANSKRIT (Hindu and Buddhist texts)

Look to this day!
For it is life, the very life of life.

In its brief course lie all the varieties and realities of your existence:
the bliss of growth,
the glory of action,
the splendour of beauty.

For yesterday is already a dream,
and tomorrow is only a vision,

But today, well-lived,
makes every yesterday a dream of happiness,
and every tomorrow a vision of hope.

Look well, therefore, to this day!
Such is the salutation of the dawn.

I Am the Bread of Life

From the CHRISTIAN BIBLE
John 6:35-40

Jesus said to them,
'I am the bread of life.
Whoever comes to me will never be hungry,
and whoever believes in me will never be thirsty.

But I said to you that you have seen me and yet do not believe.
Everything that the Father gives me will come to me,
and anyone who comes to me I will never drive away;

For I have come down from heaven,
not to do my own will,
but the will of him who sent me.

And this is the will of him who sent me,
that I should lose nothing of all that he has given me,
but raise it up on the last day.

This is indeed the will of my Father,
that all who see the Son and believe in him may have eternal life;
and I will raise them up on the last day.'

Shorter Quotes

From the CHRISTIAN BIBLE

'I am the resurrection and the life,' says the Lord. 'Those who believe in me, even though they die, will live, and everyone who lives and believes in me will never die.'

John 11.25-26

I am convinced that neither death, nor life, nor angels, nor rulers, nor things present, nor things to come, nor powers, nor height, nor depth, nor anything else in all creation, will be able to separate us
from the love of God in Christ Jesus our Lord.

Romans 8.38-39

Since we believe that Jesus died and rose again, even so, through Jesus, God will bring with him those who have died.
So we will be with the Lord for ever.
Therefore encourage one another with these words.

1 Thessalonians 4.14,17b,18

We brought nothing into the world, and we take nothing out.
The Lord gave, and the Lord has taken away;
blessed be the name of the Lord.

1 Timothy 6.7; Job 1.21b

The steadfast love of the Lord never ceases, his mercies never come to an end;
they are new every morning; great is his faithfulness.

Lamentations 3.22-23

Blessed are those who mourn, for they will be comforted.

Matthew 5.4

God so loved the world that he gave his only Son, so that everyone who believes in him may not perish but may have eternal life.

John 3.16

Music is the Language of our Souls

It has been with us since time began,
and it is important in every country
and culture across the world.

All of the major events in our societies
are accompanied by it,
and the more grand the event the
more pivotal and powerful it becomes.

It can make us laugh, cry, dance, sleep or dream.
We can be inspired to love like never before,
to fight battles with renewed courage,
to accept that which we cannot change,
to forgive and reflect,
or simply to remember another time.

Music is the language of our souls and our emotions.
It expresses that which has no words.
It reaches across countries,
ages and language boundaries,
and instantly unites us in purpose.

Never underestimate the power of music.

Modern and Popular Music

Here are some suggestions for recorded music that may be suitable for memorial activities, or simply for your own listening pleasure.

1930

Good Night Sweetheart	Guy Lombardo (also Rudy Vallee 1960)
It's Easy to Remember	Bing Crosby
Side By Side	Traditional (try Mitch Miller)
They Can't Take That Away From Me	Peggy Lee (also Frank Sinatra)

1940

I'll Be Seeing You	Bing Crosby
Now Is the Hour	Bing Crosby
Sentimental Journey	Doris Day
Somewhere Over the Rainbow	Judy Garland
Till the End of Time	Perry Como
We'll Meet Again	Vera Lynn

1950

All I Have to Do is Dream	Everley Brothers
Because of You	Tony Bennett
Harbour Lights	The Platters
My Way	Frank Sinatra
Too Young	Nat King Cole
What a Wonderful World	Louis Armstrong

1960

Comes a Time	Neil Young
Dream a Little Dream of Me	The Mamas & The Papas
Forever Young	Bob Dylan
In My Life	The Beatles
Let It Be	The Beatles
Stand By Me	Ben E King
Try to Remember (September)	Nana Mouskouri
Unchained Melody	Righteous Brothers (Used in the movie "Ghost")
You'll Never Walk Alone	Gerry & the Pacemakers

1970

As Long As I Can See the Light	Creedence Clearwater Revival
Always Look on the Bright Side	Monty Python
Bridge Over Troubled Water	Simon & Garfunkel
Bright Eyes	Simon & Garfunkel
Candle In The Wind	Elton John (Later changed for Princess Diana)
Evergreen	Barbara Streisand
Fire and Rain (See You Again)	James Taylor
Goodbye My Friend	Linda Rondstat
Hymn	Barclay James Harvest
Imagine	John Lennon
The Rose	Bette Midler
The Way We Were	Barbara Streisand
Time in a Bottle	Jim Croce
When I Get Where I'm Going	Brad Paisley & Dolly Parton
You've Got a Friend	James Taylor

1980

Baby Mine	Bette Midler (from movie "Beaches)
Carry Me (Like a Fire in your Heart)	Chris deBurgh
Dance with My Father	Luther Vandross
Don't Worry Be Happy	Bobby McFerrin
Downstream	Supertramp
Everything I Do	Bryan Adams
I've Had The Time Of My Life	Jennifer Warnes & Bill Medley
Lean on Me	Club Nouveau
Simply the Best	Tina Turner
Time After Time	Cyndi Lauper
That's What Friends Are For	Dionne Warwick
True Colors	Cyndi Lauper
Wind Beneath My Wings	Bette Midler

1990

Angels	Robbie Williams
Because You Loved Me	Celine Dion
Con Te Partiro / Say Goodbye	Andrea Bocelli & Sarah Brightman
The Dance	Garth Brooks
The Day You Went Away	Wendy Matthews
Everybody Hurts	REM
Fields of Gold	Eva Cassidy (Very reflective)
Fields of Gold	Sting (More straightforward)
Fly	Celine Dion
Hard to Say Goodbye	Boyz 2 Men
I Don't Want to Miss a Thing	Aerosmith
If I Could Be Where You Are	Enya
If I Had Only Known	Reba McEntire
If Tomorrow Never Comes	Ronan Keating
I'll Be Missing You	Puff Daddy
I'm Your Angel	Celine Dion & R Kelly
I Will Always Love You	Whitney Houston (or Dolly Parton – probably a better version for a funeral)
Lullaby – Goodnight My Angel	Billy Joel
My Heart Will Go On	Celine Dion (From the movie "Titanic")
Never Tear Us Apart	INXS
New Years Day	U2
People Get Ready	Eva Cassidy
Somewhere Over the Rainbow	Eva Cassidy
Tears In Heaven	Eric Clapton
Thankyou for the Memories	Rod Stewart
Together Again	Janet Jackson
With Or Without You	U2
You Are Not Alone	Michael Jackson
You Were Loved	Whitney Houston

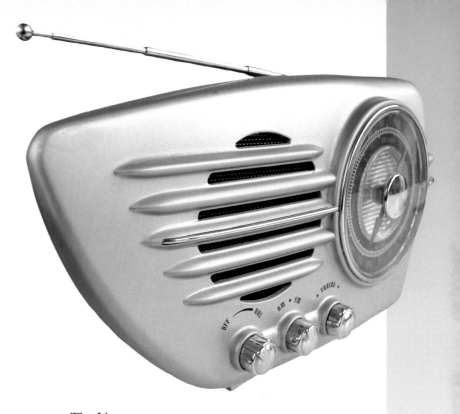

2000

Bittersweet Symphony	The Verve
Circle of Life	Elton John
Falling Into You	Kasey Chambers
Goodbye My Lover	James Blunt
If Only I Could Make Heaven Wait	Guy Sebastian
If We Never Meet Again	Selah
In the Arms of the Angels	Sarah McLachlann
I Will Remember You	Sarah McLachlan
Just Around the River Bend	from Pochahontas
Million Tears	Kasey Chambers
My Immortal	Evanescence
One Sweet Day	Mariah Carey & Boyz 2 Men
Slipped Away	Avril Lavigne
Superman	Five for Fighting
There You'll Be	Faith Hill
Time of Your Life	Green Day
To Where You Are	Josh Gorban
Who Knew	Pink
World's Greatest	R Kelly
You Raise Me Up	Westlife

Memorial DVD Music Suggestions

If you compile a background track for a Memorial DVD, consider the following points – especially if you will be sending on copies for family and friends.

- Remember that we all grieve differently. Try to consider and include as many people as possible, not exclude those who may not be familiar with the music you have chosen.

- If your pictures run more than 3 minutes, consider 3 songs (or parts of songs) in A-B-C format. Try Sad-Happy-Calm, or other combinations of the following words: peaceful, gentle, reflective, questioning, joyous, energetic, celebrate, comedy, active, travelling, beautiful, grand, wonderful, simple, nostalgic, vocal, classical, popular, less well known, original, timeless, unique, or many others!

- Be sure to listen fully to all the words, you may be surprised at what you hear when you are studying the lyrics.

- Remember that people who may not have heard your songs will assume there is a message in it for them – and they will listen intently to find it.

- There are many free programs that can help you edit songs. Please be aware of copyright issues, and do not illegally download music, sell or make a profit from your Memorial DVD without the proper legal permissions from the composers, performers and copyright holders.

Classical and Traditional Music

'When We Remember' CD contains a selection of "classical" music that would be suitable for

• A funeral or memorial gathering
• As background for a Memorial DVD
• For listening and reflection at any time

Even if you are familiar with classical music, it can sometimes be very difficult to remember the titles of music that you would like, or to find good versions of a particular piece that you would like to use.

Sometimes we enjoy a particular short melody, only to find when an excerpt of a few minutes is played, that the music wanders off into another melody that is no longer suitable.

You will probably have heard many of these melodies before, but may not know the title or composer of the piece you have listened to.

It can be very surprising to realise just how much classical music is used in movies, radio and television. Even unlikely moments such as sporting events or gardening shows are greatly enhanced by the music of the centuries-old masters. There is an enormous variety of classical music available, and it must be chosen wisely.

Take a few minutes to listen through the CD, you may be pleasantly surprised by the feelings and atmosphere that each one can suggest.

Most of the music on 'When We Remember' is instrumental, allowing listeners to be part of the experience of listening, without actually having sung words drawing our attention away from the thoughts and conversations we may be having at the time.

The vocal selections are simple and contain beautiful melodies – the words are not the main feature and the music remains the main focus when listening.

All of the excerpts pieces on 'When We Remember' are around three minutes in length, the same as popular songs that are played on the radio.

'When We Remember' Music CD

Instrumental Solos

Solo Piano	"Pathetique" Sonata 2nd Movement	Beethoven
	"Moonlight" Sonata 1st Movement	Beethoven
Solo Organ	"Jesu, Joy of Man's Desiring"	J S Bach
Solo Guitar	"Prelude No.1"	Villa-Lobos
Solo Bagpipe	Amazing Grace	Traditional
Solo Trumpet	Last Post, Reveille and Taps	Traditional

Instrumental Solos with Piano Accompaniment

Flute	"Pavanne"	Faure
Flute and Clarinet	"Sicillienne"	Faure
Cello	"The Swan" from Carnival of the Animals	Saint-Saëns
Violin	"Meditation" from Thais	Massenet

Solos with Organ or Other Accompaniment

Guitar and Strings	"Concerto de Aranjuez"	Rodrigo
Female Voice	"My Redeemer Liveth" from Messiah	Handel
	"Pie Jesu" from Requiem	Faure
Choir	"Ave Verum"	Mozart
String Quartet	"Adagio" in G minor	Albinoni
	"Canon"	Pachelbel
	"Air" from Suite No.3	J S Bach

When We Remember
CD Music Listening Guide

Music for Listening and Reflection

Professionally recorded on acoustic instruments, these individual
selections are ideal for before, during and after a gathering.
Specially arranged to include only the best-known sections of longer pieces.

Beautiful and comforting to listen to in their own right, at any time.

1 2.55 **The Swan** *from Carnival of the Animals*   Saint-Saëns (1835-1921)
Cello solo and Piano. A straightforward and graceful melody reaches ever-forward,
with clear intent and strong phrasing. Sparkling Piano imitates a beautiful sunrise
on a lake. Keywords: Calm, reflective, moderate.

2 2.16 **Sicillienne**   Faure (1845-1924)
Clarinet and Flute solo with organ accompaniment. Two instruments intertwine,
with the colours and ranges providing an ever-changing viewpoint on the wonder
of life. Keywords: Mysterious, contemplative, beautiful.

3 3.00 **Concerto de Aranjuez** *2nd Movt*   Rodrigo (1901-99)
Strings and Acoustic Guitar discuss the sorrows of life, agreeing that we are
eventually powerless to turn back the hands of time. Sad, but not without the joy
of memories. Keywords: Gentle, sorrowful, resigned.

4 3.22 **Piano Sonata "Pathetique"** *2nd Movt*   Beethoven (1770-1827)
Solo Piano performs a beautiful melody that has been much quoted in popular
song and has even appeared with words. A simple and easy-listening favourite.
Keywords: Relaxing, optimistic, sentimental.

5 3.20 **Adagio in G minor**   Albinoni (1671-1750)
Strings and Organ perform an abridged version of this deeply felt and courageous
account of grief. Albinoni's composition believes there is no escaping the inevitable
sadness, yearning and regret that death can bring.
Keywords: Sorrow, misery, acceptance.

6 2.43 Pavanne   Faure (1845-1924)

Solo Flute with simple piano accompaniment. The floating, almost ethereal sound of the Flute is explored through both low and high registers. Long phrases almost impossibly sustain through each question and reply.
Keywords: Childlike wonder, yet mature insight.

7 1.58 Prelude No. 1   Villa-Lobos (1887-1959)

Solo Guitar explores a personal point of view on change. Strong melody and chords, with lots of rubato and stretching of time, gives energy to the search for meaning.
Keywords: Masculine, direct, courageous.

8 4.08 Air *from Suite No. 3*   J S Bach (1685-1750)

Bach skilfully weaves the dance between 4 String sections, each maintaining integrity and independent purpose. With Harpsichord accompaniment, this is a beautiful and everlasting classic from the Baroque period.
Keywords: Elegant, knowing, refined.

9 2.58 Piano Sonata "Moonlight" *1st Movt*   Beethoven (1770-1827)

A simple melody resonates like a tolling bell at the passing of time, while the accompaniment weaves and changes underneath. A beautiful account of the ebb and flow of our emotions. Keywords: Romantic, reflective.

10 4.09 Meditation *from Thais*   Massenet (1842-1912)

One of Russia's finest Violinists performs this exquisite melody, accompanied by her husband on Piano. A true gem of honest communication, this rare recording is pure delight. Keywords: Emotional, vulnerable, passionate.

11 2.45 Pie Jesu *from Requiem*   Faure (1845-1924)

Solo Soprano with Organ accompaniment. The simple melody retains a childlike wonder, with limited vibrato ensuring the clarity of this beautiful ray of heavenly light from "Requiem" Keywords: Pure, grateful, simple.

12 3.12 Canon in D   Pachelbel (1653-1706)

String Quartet and Harpsichord Continuo perform this timeless classic at the perfect tempo for a respectful gathering. The interweaving melodic line is continually developed. Modern variations on the chord progression include "A Whiter Shade of Pale" and Billy Joel's "Piano Man"! Keywords: Dignified, continuity, honour.

13 2.25 I Know My Redeemer Liveth *from Messiah*   Handel (1685-1759)
A very popular and often requested classic. Solo Soprano is more expressive
and mature, with elegant Organ accompaniment and relevant English text.
Keywords: Traditional, poised, timeless.

14 2.44 Jesu, Joy of Man's Desiring   J S Bach (1685-1750)
The only solo Organ piece in this collection, this favourite would make
an ideal choice for a dignified and respectful conclusion to a funeral gathering.
Keywords: Timeless, gentle, optimistic

15 2.35 Ave Verum   Mozart (1756-91)
Full Choir and Organ perform this beautiful and moving arrangement by the master
of tuneful song. Although the text is in Latin, the intention of the honouring and
adoration is clear. Keywords: Classical, pure, reverent.

Music for Singing and Ceremony

Professionally arranged and recorded to promote participation,
and musically support group singing.

Extra long 6 seconds at the end of each track ensures
there are no "play-on" errors on the actual day.

16 2.51 The Lord is My Shepherd   Psalm 23 / "Crimond" Irvine (1836-87)
With text taken from the Christian Bible, this very popular hymn reaffirms belief
in the power of Jesus, and the comfort that this faith brings. This setting is to music
known as Crimond; there are also other melodic versions of this hymn in use.
Keywords: Traditional, comforting, affirming.

17 2.55 Going Home (Christ Gone Before)   Unknown / Dvorak (1841-1904)
This beautiful, haunting melody has its roots in folksong, and is taken from the
2nd movement from Dvorak's 9th Symphony (New World). Christian lyrics reassure
and comfort. Keywords: Beautiful, calm, wise.

18 3.07 **Abide With Me**   Lyte (1793-1847) / Monk (1823-89)

Written just weeks before his own death, Lyte's words for Evensong at his parish church have become some of the most popular of all-time. This arrangement includes Orchestra and Brass Band. Please be sure to listen right through, and take part in the complete journey. Keywords: Direct, powerful, inclusive.

19 2.48 **Going Home (Live In Me)**   Abraham / Dvorak (1841-1904)

A slightly different arrangement, down one tone, this version includes words that are secular. Respectful of all mourners, and possible variations in faith and belief. Keywords: Modern, personal, courageous.

20 3.10 **Amazing Grace** (Choir)   Newton (1725-1807) / Traditional

This well-known hymn was written by a reformed slave-trader, in the wonder of Christ revealed. Known the world over, it has become symbolic of many traditions. Opening with a solo voice, slowly but surely others gather around, uniting in comfort and strength of purpose. Keywords: Wide appeal, relevant, popular.

21 2.25 **Amazing Grace** (Bagpipe)   Traditional

Though wonderful to sing, there are many that believe the true beauty of this Celtic folksong is only revealed when performed by a lone Bagpipe. Keywords: Haunting, beautiful, dignified.

22 1.29 **Last Post**   Traditional

23 0.27 **Reveille**   Traditional

24 0.48 **Taps**   Traditional

Solo Trumpet is both defiant and vulnerable, with a human quality to the imagined words that are spoken. These bugle calls are often used daily in the Services, and are also played in tribute at the end of a soldier's life. Taps is from the American tradition, while the Last Post is of British origin. Keywords: Respect, pride, honour.

'When We Remember: Inspiration & Integrity for a Meaningful Funeral'
www.WhenWeRemember.com

Hymns and other Ceremonial Music

The Christian faith has a long tradition of hymns to select from when honouring the life of a loved one.

On **'When We Remember'** CD are the following recordings –

16 The Lord is My Shepherd
17 Going Home (Christ Gone Before)
18 Abide With Me
19 Going Home (Live in Me)
20 Amazing Grace (Choir)

Even if you are unsure as to your Christian beliefs, these hymns may be just what you are looking for as they perfectly capture many elements common to all who grieve.

If you are not generally familiar with hymns, you may be very surprised with the familiarity of the well known tunes of many of the hymns listed on the following page.

There is a centuries old tradition of dividing the church devotional day into specific periods of time.

Many of these hymns come from the period known as Evensong – praise and acknowledgement for the day that had been.

There are many more wonderful hymns that you may enjoy and find comfort in. Here are just a few suggestions -

All Things Bright and Beautiful	Lord of the Dance
And Can It Be	Make Me a Channel of Your Peace
Be Still My Soul	Morning Has Broken
Be Thou My Vision	Nearer My God to Thee
The Day Thou Gavest Lord, is Ended	O God, Our Help in Ages Past
Eternal Father, Strong to Save	The Old Rugged Cross
God of Our Fathers	Our Eyes Have Seen the Glory
Great is Thy Faithfulness	Praise My Soul, the King of Heaven
Guide Me, O Thou Great Redeemer	Swing Low, Sweet Chariot
Here I Am Lord	Thine Be the Glory
How Great Thou Art	To God be the Glory, Great Things He Hath Done
Jerusalem	What a Friend We Have in Jesus
The King of Love My Shepherd Is	
Lead Us, Heavenly Father	
Lord of All Hopefulness	

Abide With Me

Music: "Eventide" William H. Monk, 1861

A - bide with me, fast falls the ev - en tide

The dark - ness deep - ens Lord, with me a - bide

When earth - ly help - ers fail, and com - forts flee

Help of the help - less, Lord a - bide with me

Abide With Me

Words: Henry F. Lyte, 1847

Abide with me; fast falls the eventide;
The darkness deepens; Lord with me abide.

When earthly helpers fail and comforts flee,
Help of the helpless, O abide with me.

I fear no foe, with Thee at hand to bless;
Ills have no weight, and tears no bitterness.

Where is death's sting? Where, grave, thy victory?
I triumph still, if Thou abide with me.

Hold Thou Thy cross before my closing eyes;
Shine through the gloom and point me to the skies.

Heaven's morning breaks, and Earth's vain shadows flee;
In life, in death, O Lord, abide with me.

Amazing Grace

Music: Traditional Celtic / Gaelic

Amazing Grace

Words: John Newton 1725 – 1807

Amazing Grace! How sweet the sound
That saved a wretch like me!
I once was lost, but now am found;
Was blind, but now I see.

'Twas Grace that taught my heart to fear,
And Grace my fears relieved;
How precious did that Grace appear
The hour I first believed.

Through many dangers, toils and snares,
I have already come;
'Tis Grace that brought me safe thus far,
And Grace will lead me home.

When we've been there ten thousand years,
Bright shining as the sun,
We've no less days to sing God's praise
Than when we'd first begun.

Amazing Grace! How sweet the sound
That saved a wretch like me!
I once was lost, but now am found;
Was blind, but now I see.

The Lord's My Shepherd

Music: "Crimond"

The Lord's My Shepherd

Words: Psalm 23 Arr Francis Rous 1579 – 1659

The Lord's my Shepherd, I'll not want;
He makes me down to lie
In pastures green; He leadeth me
The quiet waters by.

My soul He doth restore again
And me to walk doth make
Within the paths of righteousness,
Even for His own name's sake.

Yea, though I walk in death's dark vale
Yet will I fear no ill;
For Thou art with me, and Thy rod
And staff my comfort still.

My table Thou hast furnished me
In presence of my foes;
My head Thou dost with oil anoint,
And my cup overflows.

Goodness and mercy all my life
Shall surely follow me;
And in God's house forevermore,
My dwelling place shall be.

Going Home (You Will Live In Me)

Music: From Dvorak "New World Symphony" 2nd Movt
Arr: J Abraham

Is it like go-ing home, when death calls you near? Hear my voice, feel my love, Help to dry my tears.

Where are you? Near or far? Gone with mornings tide? Why can I hear you still? Are you by my side?

Set your sail, Spirit free, Earthly cares are gone. Love re-mains strong and clear, I will carry on.

Going Home
(You Will Live In Me)

Words: M Abraham

Is it like going home,
When death calls you near?
Hear my voice, feel my love,
Help to dry my tears

Where are you? Near or far? Gone with morning's tide?
Why can I hear you still? Are you by my side?

Set your sail, spirit free,
Earthly cares now gone,
Love remains, strong and clear,
I will carry on

Sorrow stings, heal my pain,
Guide me now in peace,
Comfort me, hold me close,
Fears my tears release

Softly now, close the door, now the day is through,
Every thought, every word, I'll remember you

All we shared still remains,
Let my promise be
Strong and clear, hear my song,
You will live in me

Going Home (Christ Has Gone Before)

Music: From Dvorak "New World Symphony" 2nd Movt
Arr: J Abraham

Go - ing home, mo - ving on through God's op- en door, Hush my soul have no fear, Christ has gone be- fore.

Part - ing hurts, love pro tests, pain is not de- nied; Yet in Christ, love and hope span the great di- vide.

Go - ing home, mov - ing on, through God's op-en door, Hush my soul, have no fear, Christ has gone be fore.

Going Home
(Christ Has Gone Before)

Words: Unknown

Going home, moving on,
Through God's open door;
Hush my soul, have no fear,
Christ has gone before

Parting hurts, love protests, pain is not denied;
Yet in Christ, love and hope span the great divide

Going home, moving on,
Through God's open door;
Hush my soul, have no fear,
Christ has gone before

No more guilt, no more fear,
All the past is healed;
Broken dreams now restored,
Perfect grace revealed

Christ has died, Christ is ris'n, Christ will come again;
Death destroyed, life restored, love alone shall reign

Going home, moving on,
Through God's open door;
Hush my soul, have no fear,
Christ has gone before

After the Funeral

It is a sad but absolute truth that life and death are always partners. One must follow the other.

We tell ourselves we understand this, yet we are never fully prepared for the reality of when a loved one dies.

Every person, every relationship, every circumstance, every belief will be part of the unique experience that you have at this time.

Some deaths are expected, some are not. Sometimes our previous experiences with death will provide great comfort, and at other times our past losses will only feel closer to hand.

You may find that you are very calm, especially if you have been able to care for somebody well in the time leading up to an expected death. You will of course feel sadness in the moments ahead that you miss their physical presence, but your preparation may bring peace as well as sorrow.

You may feel emotions that surprise you. Shock can play a part in many ways. You could feel anything from acceptance to numbness and disbelief, through to complete breakdown and temporary absence of coping skills.

> Even the longest, most difficult journey starts with one small step

If the death of a loved one is completely unexpected and unprepared for, then you will need to accept that it will take time for the new reality to sink in.

Our brains and bodies are wonderfully designed to cope with stress in many ways, and you will need to accept every one of your emotions as they rise and fall in the days ahead.

> "Losing my father was so just different to when we lost Helen.
>
> One death we were prepared for – we had months of sharing precious moments and in the end we all knew that it was just the way of things.
>
> We cried and grieved, but we also laughed... it was sad yet it was also ok somehow.
>
> But when Helen went – the shock was so overwhelming. Nobody could believe it. Nobody was prepared. How can you prepare for something like that?"

Please be sure to contact close friends and family for support. This is a time of accepting help, of being flexible in your expectations of others and yourself, and understanding that we are all vulnerable.

Let people help you. Talk, touch and hug, laugh, cry, be childlike, be emotional, be strong at times if you must, but try to take each hour and day one at a time.

Children and animals are often far more resilient than adults, and with good reason. They do not look too far back, or too far forward. Try to accept each moment exactly as it is. Today is also precious.

As you travel through the next few days and weeks, there may be decisions to be made and you will probably find that you are not able to concentrate as you would like.

There is a logical way forward, and each step along the way has a variety of things to consider and decisions to be made.

Start at the beginning, and move through the process of each stage. Information is given a piece at a time and decisions will be made in turn.

You do not have to deal with everything all at once – in fact your thoughts will become clearer and more in tune with your individual needs as time passes.

"We loved our elderly parents dearly. My mother's death
separated our adult family – we just didn't know how to cope.
Yet, a few years later, my father's death brought us closer than
ever before. Two different reactions to the power of love."

"I remember, a few months later, laughing so much that
my sides hurt. It was a real turning point – I wasn't "finished with grief",
but I was learning to live with it."

"Once my brother was gone, I couldn't shake the feeling of loneliness.
There was nobody left that shared my early memories. But then I saw
my grandson's delight at catching his first fish. Maybe new memories
are just as precious as old ones? That's what my brother would say."

"Compiling my dear grandmother's Memorial DVD
was such an amazing, healing process. Suddenly she
wasn't just an old lady; she was also a young mother, a daughter,
and even once a grand-daughter like me."

"I had so much more I wanted to share with him.
A friend suggested I talk to him anyway. You know what?
If I listen really carefully, by the time I ask him a question,
I already know what he'd say. Funny thing that."

"We loved each other so much. I know she'd want me to be happy.
I'll try. What else can you do?"

Small Steps Forward

In the days following a funeral, try to gently balance the demands of modern life with your responsibility to look after yourself.

There are often many things still to do, and many decisions still to make.

Most of these financial and legal details can wait, at least a day or two, while you pause to gather your strength.

Keep busy, but don't push yourself.

Be independent, but allow others to help.

Take things as they come, and resist the temptation to look too far ahead.

You are still travelling through grief, and the road is never straight or simple to navigate.

Financial and Legal Considerations

There may be many financial and legal considerations to attend to when someone dies. Depending on their age and relationship to you, it may mean that the decisions and paperwork of the last few days are only part of the many things you must attend to when someone dies.

It does not help to list here all the possible organisations and details that may need your attention in the next few weeks. The list would be far too long, and probably mostly irrelevant to your particular circumstances. It could seem overwhelming and impossible to complete.

Attending to financial and legal considerations is one area where it is definitely an advantage to enlist the help of others. Contact a trusted friend, relative or professional advisor and allow them to help you.

It can be very upsetting to be telephoning or writing for hours, constantly retelling the death of your loved one. There are certain things that only you can authorise or sign, and you will have to be very involved at many levels along the way. But just as busy or stressed executives have a personal secretary, you should do the same.

Many organisations will need a copy of the Death Certificate, and will then complete the changes required for you and follow up with some new paperwork for you to sign. Some countries have government departments that are interlinked, and will be able to make many of the changes you need from one central authority.

You should expect everybody you deal with to be sympathetic at this time, and do not get upset if you find difficult individuals along the way. Simply call back later, or get someone else to deal with the complications for you.

Some of the possible organisations and people
that may need your attention –

Legal
Registration of Death
Reading and Enacting of a Will
Joint ownership of assets (house, shares, car etc)

Financial
Funeral Directors and associated services
Banking Accounts
Government assistance or pensions
Work related contracts

Community
Sporting or Cultural groups
Health Care

Keep a clear list of –

• *Who* you have made contact with

The organisation and the name of the person you dealt with

• *When* this was done

Include the date, time, and remember to list each time
you made contact

• Any *follow up* details you may need to attend to

This could include if they are sending you forms, or if you need to wait for other details to be completed first.

Now is not the time to rely on your memory. If others are helping you, they will need an accurate record of where you are up to in each transaction.

Your Funeral Director can be an excellent source of information and assistance in getting you started. They will often have the ability to organise some matters for you, or have a list of contact details for your national or local area.

Thank You and Memorials

There will be many people who have helped you in the past few days, and will continue to help you in the time ahead.

Perhaps you have been reunited with friends and family that you have not seen for a while, or perhaps people very close to you have really stepped up in their thoughtful care at this time. They may have helped organise catering, or picked up a relative from the airport, or just managed to do the right thing at the right time.

There may be people that have assisted you in a professional capacity. This could include medical staff, religious leaders and funeral celebrants, and any goods and services providers that may have been outstanding in their timely and considerate delivery.

Sometimes there is a complete stranger that can play an enormous role when somebody dies, and by fate or coincidence they are the ones to help when you need it most.

When we think of others, we are temporarily transported from our own sadness into a feeling of gratefulness, of trust, of hope.

Many cultures have the saying "It is better to give than receive." We can feel helpless and powerless when somebody dies, but it is still possible to accept help graciously, and not lose a sense of who we are.

All things have a time, and now is your time to receive. Some people may be very uncomfortable with this. You may need to actively set about letting others that you will be ok, that you appreciate all that they are doing for you, and that some day you will be strong enough to return the favour.

Everybody that you have been in contact with in the last few days knows that you are grateful. They do not expect you to do anything, and perhaps you will simply not be up to communicating your feelings for a while.

If this is the case, do not feel pressured. People helped you because they wanted to; they would do anything to relive your sadness at this time.

The best "thankyou" is for you to do what you need to do – whatever allows you to move through your grief.

On the following pages are some ideas for saying "thankyou".

Thank You for Those Who Attend

Condolence Reply

You may wish to consider a gesture or small gift to say thankyou to those who attended the funeral.

Most often this is simply a matter of recording the names, and then sending a simple thankyou card for their attendance and condolences. Do not be pressured into organising these straight away – as long as you have some record of those who attended it may be weeks before these cards are sent. People will understand.

Sometimes it can be appropriate to consider a more active or immediate way to say thankyou. There are some traditional and modern options to consider –

Cycle of Life

Give a reminder of the cycle of life and the beauty of nature. Seeds before summer and bulbs after summer will provide a lasting display for the passing of a loved one in the weeks to come. You may find that certain flowers or plants are an obvious choice.

Charity Donations

If you have asked for donations to be made to a particular charity or organisation (for example a Cancer Research institute), you may find that the organisation receiving the donations may have thankyou cards or perhaps information brochures on how the donations will be used.

Rosemary

A sprig of rosemary is the traditional emblem of remembrance. Ancient Greek scholars would keep rosemary close by while they worked, or wear a sprig behind their ear during examinations. It was believed that rosemary increases our power to remember.

Order of Service

If you had an Order of Service for the funeral it will make a special keepsake for those who attended, and it could be sent to those that could not be there on the day.

Photographs

Photographs can easily be scanned and digitally reproduced on printed thankyou cards sent after the funeral. You have the advantage of less time pressure if you choose to do this after a funeral.

Poetry or Verse

As part of a written thankyou you may wish to include a special poem, verse or saying that was important to the person who died, or one that reflects the feelings of the family that remains.

Both of the previous ideas are particularly powerful if there are some mourners who are unable to attend through distance or illness. You could also consider an audio recording of part or all of the gathering – it would be a very strong and treasured token for those who were absent on the day.

A Further Thought

There are many ways to say thankyou, and we all do so differently. Do not be concerned if you do none of these things. Everybody will understand that you are doing the best you can under very difficult and draining circumstances.

You may find that your good intentions do not go ahead because you simply do not have the energy to concentrate on getting anything other than the essentials done.

While you may wish to pass on your feelings of gratitude and thankfulness, now is not the time to particularly focus on the feelings of others.

Music CD

If the music used in a funeral or memorial was particularly appropriate or representative of the person that died, consider making up CDs of the music and passing them on to friends and family that attend.

Memorial DVD

If a collection of photos has been crafted into a short DVD to be played at the service, then you could also consider making multiple copies of this for the mourners.

> Every person that attends will have one clear wish for you –
> *that you cope with grief
> in your own way
> at your own time,
> and that you find peace
> as soon as you are able.*

Memorials

A memorial is a focus on a life lived. It can generally take two forms, and decisions on memorials often become clearer as time goes on.

It is possible to do one or both, according to the wishes and characteristics of the person that has died, and the family and friends that remain.

- Fixed or physical memorial
- Memorial gathering or activity

Fixed or Physical Memorial

A physical memorial can be a permanent marker for a life lived.

Family, friends and unknown future generations can come to a specific location to remember and pay respects to their heritage.

You may have already decided on how and where you wish to place a memorial to your loved one. There is no need to hurry this decision, and you may well find that you will feel differently in the weeks or even months ahead.

It is perfectly usual for a memorial to become more important as time goes on. Many families have decided to place a memorial decades after the death of someone. Other families will restore a memorial centuries old. We can never know the ways in which a memorial may be significant in the time to come.

Traditional Memorial

If you have chosen a traditional burial or will place ashes in a dedicated area, then you will need to decide on the style and wording of the memorial.

Some areas may use a metal or stone memorial, and the variations available are great. It can take many weeks for this to be produced, and there is no rush to complete your final tribute.

Remember to consider the surrounding memorials when you make your choice. It is respectful to both your family and the families surrounding you, and occasionally there will be a particular protocol or style to follow. If you are unsure, just ask.

Take your time, perhaps visit the area with a friend, and have a look around at what others have chosen.

There may be a clear cultural or religious tradition you wish to follow.

Perhaps a certain memorial appeals to you because of the theme or the way it was created. If you see one that particularly appeals, feel free to ask staff how and where it was created.

Many memorials are crafted by people that are proud of their traditions or creativity, and will be only to happy to discuss options with you.

There are no rules as to what legally constitutes a memorial. You are often free to respectfully do whatever best suits you and your family.

No Memorial

Perhaps you have decided to scatter ashes in a specific location. Perhaps you have opted for a woodland burial with only a tree or plant as a marker.

You may decide at a later date to erect a memorial in memory of your loved one at this or another location, or to start a small book that contains details of where ashes were scattered so that others yet to be born may know. There is time to decide, and your feelings may change as time goes on.

Other Ideas

Discussions with friends and family, your Funeral Director, or an internet search will reveal many options for creating a memorial.

Some may be surprising or unusual, but rest assured that if there is a company that offers a particular product, then you will not be the first family to choose it! Perhaps some of the following ideas will prompt your own unique way of remembering someone that has died.

Garden Seat

You will need to approach your local council for permission, but it can be surprising how supportive a community authority may be about erecting a seat in a public place, with a memorial plaque attached in a public place.

Name a Star

Although you will not get to visit it, you will certainly get to see your star named in honour of a person that has died. A certificate is sent to you, recognising the official name.

Start a Foundation

Sometimes we are in position to offer financial support to organisations that need public funding to continue.

Donations could start at the funeral, and continue with fundraising events and other ideas to increase public awareness.

You could aim for a large foundation, supporting a community awareness or medical service, or simply a small annual scholarship in your loved one's honour.

Create a Reef

Some people are very enthusiastic about giving back to the natural world, and helping to create a reef offshore for fish and other marine life can be a very fitting tribute.

Jewellery and Ornaments

Ashes can be placed into many items tastefully by jewellers that are sympathetic to your request. This may be inappropriate for you to consider, or it may create a meaningful family heirloom to treasure.

Some companies can create candles with images on them, or perhaps you can engrave certain items with meaningful words.

Start or Join a Website

There are many sites dedicated to hosting your loved one's web page. Options range from simply placing words, photos and music for other to view, through to an interactive and ever-changing site that allows you and others to remember them in your daily lives and activities. Some sites are perpetually funded by charitable organisations to ensure they will always be available.

Create a "LifeBook"

Sometimes we need to gather photos, music, thoughts and other items into one place, in honour of a person that died. Perhaps we create a DVD and send copies to others, engage a writer to record in print a life story, or perhaps we decorate a wooden box and place precious memories inside. There are many possibilities for creating your own personal family memorial.

Memorial Gathering or Activity

Sometimes it is very appropriate or important for people to gather again, at a certain time after a funeral.

Many people comment that the actual time of a funeral can seem quite "unreal". When friends and family choose to meet again at a later, significant date, it is a further chance to -

• Celebrate a life lived

• Acknowledge more fully the loss that is felt

• Create and cherish the "collective memory" for those that remain

• Use the luxury of less time pressure to truly create a meaningful farewell

• Gather support during the months following a death, when grief and the effects of a loss is often strongest in it's reality.

Perhaps the person that died had a particular day that was "theirs" for example a birthday, significant anniversary, or another date that was very significant that they would definitely have liked to have been involved in.

Often the placing of a headstone, cremation plaque, or other marker in the months ahead is a wonderful chance to mark a life lived.

Following are some ideas that may appeal to you if you are considering a Memorial Gathering.

There are as many possibilities as there are personalities in this world.

You know the person that died.

What would they have particularly approved of?

What would they really enjoy?

Releasing the Spirit

The release of butterflies or birds can be a wonderful way of "setting free the spirit" and allowing those present to participate in a practical way to creating memories.

In recent years companies have emerged that supply these services, with great consideration to the treatment of the creatures they release. For example, the natural habitat of the release area is considered, to ensure the comfortable transition of the particular species of butterfly or bird to be released.

Helium balloons are also a choice for releasing at a memorial gathering.

They can provide a spectacular and moving display of colour as they are released to follow the breeze. Some people, however, are concerned for the environmental impact of the balloons as they eventually land and settle.

Sometimes it can be very meaningful to release a "message in a bottle" or a floral wreath at a significant body of water.

A Celebration of Life

If you really want to create a feeling of "celebrating a life lived", then there are many opportunities to do this in a truly individual or memorable way.

Families have let off fireworks, staged a concert, cooked a traditional feast, delighted in displays of skydiving, motorbike parades, fire truck water fountains, ceremonial church bells, and many other experiences.

Perhaps the person that died was particularly enthusiastic about a particular activity or lifestyle. Consider a golf day, volunteering en masse to walk dogs at the local animal shelter, cleaning up the vegetation or planting trees at a particular public place, helping out at mealtimes at the local care home, or many other ideas.

It can be fabulous to truly "connect" with the personality and ideals of the person that has died. Almost anything that your group does together will ensure a memorable and meaningful experience, in honour of a loved one.

Set aside some time to imagine, time to consider or reflect, and see what you come up with.

It is not unusual to want to honour the memory of somebody by focussing on the cause of death and speaking out, to warn or rally others to try to prevent the sad event from occurring again in the future.

Examples include those that die through drink driving, drug use, mental illness, and other misfortunes. Also included are those who have died from a disease for which we believe a cure may be found someday.

Families have asked mourners to donate financial, time or other support to a relevant charity or research organisation, so that the gathering may feel that the person had "not died in vain" and perhaps through their death something can be contributed for the common good of all.

A Further Thought

Consider that sometimes we are truly able to honour someone best when we use our life as a memorial.

If we know that a loved one would want to see us happy and living our lives with purpose and grace, then we can strive to do this in the best way we can.

Seeking Greater Meaning

Some people are able to find purpose in death, and it is very possible for the dead to help the living in this way.

If a death is unexpected or traumatic, or of a young or vulnerable person, then we can be especially challenged to make sense of what has happened.

Many of our greatest and most inspired moments occur at times of extreme stress; when we are forced to evaluate exactly what is important and how best we might spend our remaining days in this life.

Grief Resources

It is beyond the scope of this book to cover all that needs to be said about grief and loss. We are all unique, we all have different personalities and experiences, and each death will find us in different circumstances to the one before.

You are not alone in your grief, however, and now is not the time to "be strong" and resist your feelings.

Accept help, have courage, and start to move through your grief. You do not have to travel this journey alone.

Grief is of course a universal experience, but each of us will find comfort in the different approaches of a wide variety of sources, both old and new.

Old Friends

Sometimes all we need is a listening ear, gentle support and guidance, and time to incorporate the enormous change into our lives.

Sympathy, understanding, inspiration, comfort, familiarity of routine, shelter in the strength of others – all are powerful healers.

Age-old sayings have usually stood the test of time because they hold a truth that is common to all who live and love.

Here are some to consider –

"It is better to have loved and lost, than to never have loved at all."
The deeper we love, the more we open ourselves to loss. Many people say they can eventually accept the sorrow of death, because they have known the joyous happiness of love.

"They live on in our hearts"
Whatever your spiritual beliefs, when we share experiences with someone, our memory is not diminished by their passing. All that was done remains done, all that was shared remains shared. You may even find that your future thoughts and actions are shaped by the person that has died. Surely this is truly "living on" in a very real way.

"No one is an island"
People are such wonderfully complex beings, with immense capacity for influencing each other. When we feel the disconnection of grief, it can be surprising to realise the strength we can gain by simply spending time with others. Even when we don't feel like it.

*"They would have wanted you
to be happy"*
As painful as this can sometimes be to
hear, eventually we can start to see that
true love is a positive influence, even
when separated by death. When the
time is right, feel free to smile, to laugh,
or even to rejoice in the beauty of a
loved shared. Don't worry, be happy.

"Keep busy"
This is great advice, providing you
are **actively** working through your
grief, not **avoiding** your grief.
Routines can be a great source of
comfort. Helping others helps us to
feel better too. Try keeping a diary
of your thoughts, it can be an excellent
way to work through private feelings,
especially when you are not up to
talking. Set small, achievable goals
for each day, or week. Care for yourself.

"One day at a time"
Because today, when all is said and
done, is all we have. Your emotions
will rise and fall many times as you
bring the change of death into reality.
Looking too far ahead can be very
difficult, because we assume that
we will feel then as we do right now.

There are many more sayings that
refer to periods of stress and change.

Which ones are your favourites?

How would you advise yourself
at this time?

Put "yourself" in a chair, and then
sit down opposite and start talking.

You might be surprised with how
wise and compassionate you really are.

New Friends

Sometimes it is easier, or necessary, to seek help from others outside our close companions. We may have experienced a complicated grief, or be working with emotions that are out of our capacity to deal with at this time.

Sometimes we don't want to "burden" those close to us. Or perhaps our friends are there to help us enjoy the good times, rather than remind us of the sad times.

Sometimes we are doing well in the first few days or weeks following a death, and then discover that things are not continuing as we would like.

Do not be surprised, or embarrassed, if you find that you need help at this particular point in your life. The death of a loved one can challenge us on so many levels.

We can re-examine and challenge every belief we had previously held so dear.

Our spiritual, physical, emotional and intellectual concepts may never be the same again. It is a real strength to admit that we are vulnerable.

Here are some suggestions to help you begin –

- Community doctors and nurses
- Mental health specialists (counsellors, psychologists, psychiatrists)
- Religious groups & churches
- Government sponsored support groups
- Private organisations and courses
- Self-help books
- Internet research
- Online support and discussion groups

There is help available – reach out and you will find many others waiting to help you along.

The information on the following pages was taken from www.caringinfo.org

Overview

Grief is how one reacts to a loss.

Grief reactions may be experienced in response to physical losses, such as a death or in the response to symbolic or social losses such as a divorce or loss of a job.

All loss involves the absence of someone loved or something that fulfils a significant need in one's life.

Grief may be experienced in the combination of mental, physical, or social reactions.

- Mental/emotional reactions can include anger, guilt, anxiety, sadness, and despair

- Physical reactions can include sleeping problems, changes in appetite, physical problems, or illness

- Social reactions can include feelings about taking care of others in the family, role changes in the family, returning to work, or differences in social situations.

There is no right or wrong way to grieve after a significant loss. Most discover how to eventually move on with life, even though the grief experience is a difficult and trying time.

Coping styles depend on one's personality and their relationship with the person who has died. This experience can also be affected by one's cultural and religious background, coping skills, mental history, and their support system.

Taking care of yourself, and accessing the support of friends and family, can help a person get through difficult times.

Bereavement

Bereavement is the period after a loss during which grief is experienced.

The time spent in a period of bereavement depends on how attached the person was to the person who died, and how much time was spent anticipating the loss.

Some view the process of bereavement as having 4 phases:

Shock and numbness

Usually occurring soon after a death, this is evident when the person finds it difficult to believe the death has occurred; is feeling stunned and numb.

Yearning and searching

As shock and numbness recede, there remains the tendency to "forget" the person has died. Perhaps one catches a glimpse of somebody who reminds them of the deceased, or you expect them to be there when you first arrive home.

Disorganisation and despair

As the reality of the absence of the person who died settles in, it is common to feel depressed and find it difficult to think about the future. You may be easily distracted, or have difficulty concentrating and focusing on any one task.

Reorganisation

As one slowly makes the adjustment to all the ways in his or her life that have changed as a result of the loss, a sense of reorganisation and renewal begins to evolve.

Life is forever changed after a significant loss, but you slowly learn how the different aspects of your life become reprioritised as you "pick up the pieces" and begin to move on.

It is not that you forget about the person who died, but you have begun to learn how to live with this knowledge.

Some Common Questions

What is grief?

Grief is the normal response of sorrow, emotion, and confused emotions that come from the loss of someone or something important to you.

It is a natural part of life.

Grief is a typical reaction to death, divorce, job loss, a move away from family and friends, or loss of good health due to illness.

How does grief feel?

Following a death or loss, you may feel empty and numb, as if you are in shock.

You may notice physical changes such as trembling, nausea, trouble breathing, muscle weakness, dry mouth, or trouble sleeping and eating.

You may become angry – at a situation, a particular person, or just angry in general.

Guilt is a common response which may be easier to accept and overcome by looking at the experience in terms of "regret". When we think "I regret I was not in the room when he died" or "I regret I was not able to speak more openly about dying" it is less critical than "I feel guilty about my behaviour".

People in grief may have strange or disturbing dreams, be absent-minded, withdraw socially, or lack the desire to participate in activities that used to be enjoyable.

While these feelings and behaviours are normal during grief, they will pass.

How long does grief last?

Grief lasts as long as it takes you to accept and learn to live with your loss. For some people, this is a few months. For others, it may take years.

The length of time spent grieving is different for each person. There are many reasons for the differences, including personality, health, coping style, culture, family background, other stressors and life experiences.

The time spent grieving also depends on your relationship with the person lost and how prepared you were for the loss.

How will I know when I'm done grieving?

After a significant loss, you may be consumed and overwhelmed by the grief reactions you are experiencing.

In time, as the reality of the loss sinks in, and all the changes as a result of the loss have been experienced, you will learn to adjust to living without the physical presence of the person who died.

Eventually, even after significant loss, you will realize you are grieving less as you discover renewed energy in living. You will become less consumed by the impact of the loss and begin to draw comfort rather than pain from the memories. In a sense, you are never "done grieving."

With a significant loss, there will always be moments when you will remember the loss, and perhaps you experience some of the feelings of grief.

Fortunately, the time period between these surges will lengthen considerably as you learn how to cope with your loss.

Bibliography – 'When We Remember' Series

Funeral & Memorial Service Readings, Poems & Tributes	Baum, Rachel (Ed)	McFarland 1999
Psychosocial Aspects of Death and Dying	Canine	McGraw-Hill 1996
Complete Guide to Funeral Planning: How to Arrange the Appropriate Service	Carnell	Lyons Press 2005
World Religions	Catoir	St Pauls 1992, update 2003
Simply Essential Funeral Planning Kit	Cochrane	Self Counsel Press 2002
Remember Me: A Lively Tour of the New American Way of Death	Cullen	Harper Collins 2006
Music is the Voice of All Sorrow, All Joy	Exley	Exley Publications 1992
To Someone Special in Times of Trouble	Exley	Exley Publication 1999
Words of Comfort	Exley	Exley Publication 1999
At Journey's End: The Complete Guide To Funerals and Funeral Planning	Fatteh, Abdullah & Naaz	Health Info 1999
Remembrances and Celebrations: A book of Eulogies, Elegies, Letters and Epitaphs	Harris, Jill (Ed)	Random House 1999
What to Do When Somebody Dies: How to deal with the Practical Arrangements that have to be Made after a Death	Harris	Which UK 2005

Christians Grieve Too	Howard, Donald	Banner of Truth UK USA 1979
Last Wishes: A Funeral Planning Manual & Survivors Guide	James & Lyn	Mavami 2000
How Different Religions View Death and Afterlife	Johnson et al	Charles Press 1998
Complete Book of Funeral Planning Readings & Music: How to plan and organise the funeral your loved ones would most appreciate	Johnstone, Gibbs & Wynburne	Foulsham 2005
On Death and Dying: What the dying have to teach doctors, nurses, clergy and their own families	Kubler-Ross	Scribner 1969
A Humanist Funeral Service	Lamont Corliss	Prometheus 1954, 1977
Saying Goodbye Your Way: Planning or Buying a Funeral or Cremation for Yourself or Someone You Love	Llewellyn, John	Tropico Press 2004
For Weddings and a Funeral: Special Poems for Special Occasions	Marsden, John	Pan McMillan 1996, 2006
Perfect Stranger's Guide to Funerals and Greiving Practices: A Guide to Etiquette in Other People's Religious Ceremonies	Matlins	Skylight Paths 2000
Dealing Creatively with Death	Morgan, Ernest	Upper Access 2001
Readings for Remembrance: A Collection for Funerals and Memorial Services	Munro, Eleanor (Ed)	Penguin Books 2000

In Memorium: A Guide to Modern Funeral and Memorial Services	Searl	Skinner House Books 2000
In Preparation: How to Have a Funeral	Shaw & Shaw	Readsome 2002
For My Family: A Legacy for Future Generations	Stone	New Holland 2004
Final Celebrations	Sublette & Flagg	Pathfinder 1992
Winning Ways: The Funeral Profession's Guide to Human Relations	Van Beck, Todd	Appleton 1999
Funerals Without God: A Practical Guide to Non-Religious Funerals	Wilson	Prometheus 1990
Creating Meaningful Funeral Ceremonies: A Guide for Families	Wolfelt	Companion Press 2000
Creating Meaningful Funeral Ceremonies: A Guide for Caregivers	Wolfelt	Companion Press 2003
Remembering Well: Rituals for Celebrating Life and Mourning Death	York, Sarah	Wiley 2000
Forever Remembered	Zadra & Woodard	Compendium Inc 2003

Thankyou

So many people have given so freely of their time, expertise, emotional energy and plain old encouragement. Everybody seemed to instinctively recognise the importance of the project, and I am forever grateful for your generosity of spirit.

For wise counsel, uncompromising support
and generous sharing of experience –

Jenny Alexander, Lana Allison, Lyn Anderson, Timur Arutyunyan,
Michelle Clendining, Penny Coucil, John & Rosie Cox, Susan Dado, Tonia Davies,
Ann Dorey, Gill Evans, Dr Chris Farmer, Trevor Francis-Jones, Rob Goode,
Scott Harris, Alexey Kornilov, Larry McCabe, Nikita Obukhov, Regula Odermatt,
Rosemary Osborne, Lydia Pearson, Bibi Pey, Dr Frank Quinn, Rev John Reid,
Fabian Reisner, Jan Siering, Luiz Sena, Alan Smith, Nikki Smith, Peter Stewart fms,
Alan Stokes, Ian Strathie, Steve Wright, the Very Rev John Young.

Songs of praise to the magnificent music team –

Jim Abraham, Ross A'hern, Dr Carlos Alvarado, Karen Ashworth, Daniel Barnett,
Elaine Beckett, Michael Bennett, Daniel Brown, Brad Child, Greg Crittendon,
Iva Davies, Deborah de Graaff, Jane Hennessy, Simon Leadley, Leah Lock,
Alexandra Loukianova, LVS Choir, Manly-Warringah Choir, Michelle Ollson,
Rosemary Osborne, Robert Pearce, Lionel Robinson, Tim Ryan, Lorraine Silk,
Verity Snook, Murilo Tanouye, Sue Taylor, Antonia Todorova, Brydon Stace,
Dan Walker, Steve Watson, Ami Williamson, Andrew Wilson, Naira Yusofova.

At the business end of making things actually happen –

Emerson Brantley, Jennifer Harris, William Inglis, Karen McCreadie,
Lyle McNeish, Nigel Walker, Tim Yuan, Jean Zhu, Trackdown Studios,
all the incredible team at Melbourne IT and a special mention to
Rob Baker at GoDesign.net.au for beautifully efficient graphic design,
and for sharing the vision for the project from the very early stages!

Dedicated to

The unknown person at Loquat Valley
who slipped a note into my handbag that simply read...

"We were with you in your happiness
and we are still with you now"

With love to the two people that confirmed
my faith in the importance of the project
'When We Remember'

Nellie Anderson nee Jurd (27 June 1912 – 17 March 2006)
Frank Clendining (29 December 1936 – 2 March 2007)

And of course to my irreplaceable, wise, patient
and unwaveringly loving husband

Jim

*"To love is to take the greatest risk of all.
It is to place one's future and one's happiness into another's hands.
It is to allow oneself to trust without reserve.
It is to accept vulnerability.
And thus I love you."*

Helen Thompson (1943 –)

Melissa Abraham
B.Mus.Ed., L.T.C.L., MACE

Melissa is a highly respected educator, and a talented classical and jazz musician. She feels blessed to have performed and conducted in the UK, Europe, Australia, New Zealand and USA for 20 years. Like most of us, she is no stranger to the great joys and terrible sorrows that life, and loss, can deal to us.

Her skills and training have often been called on to bring inspiration and integrity to the final services for her lost loved ones, and professionally for other families as well.

Through these experiences, she has learned intimately the vital emotional role a memorial event plays in our lives, and the long-term issues that avoiding the grieving process can bring. All too often she has found few resources to help personalise this process, other than verbal suggestions and standard hymnal and readings.

And so she began this journey; a passion to create a single-source guide, in a very user-friendly format, that meaningfully acknowledges the delicate balance of emotional and practical needs at this time.

Her exhaustive research and consultation was guided by many skilled hands, including funeral directors, religious leaders, secular celebrants, psychologists and of course many generous individuals and families. The result is a comprehensive roadmap that brings together all aspects of funeral planning to assist a family through this stressful period of decision making.

'When We Remember' focuses on the critical first week following a death – an emotional crisis period when clear information and guidance are most needed. This unique, generous and highly acclaimed resource draws on many decades of experiences, particularly in understanding the power of music and prose in the rituals of our lives.

Melissa currently lives in Sydney, Australia with 2 dogs, 3 chickens and 1 husband, Jim!

Symphony *"sounding together"*
Sympathy *"feeling together"*
Synergy *"being together"*

When We Remember Series

When We Remember is an internationally acclaimed series to assist families
and professionals in creating meaningful funerals.

When We Remember IIMF   *ISBN 9780980351002*
Inspiration & Integrity for a Meaningful Funeral
228 page hardcover book & CD
Complete planning guide before and after a death.
Recommended by Funeral Director Associations world-wide.

When We Remember CITS   *ISBN 9780980351033*
Comfort & Inspiration in Time of Sorrow
168 page hardcover book & CD
Perfect Condolence gift and Memorial Book, including
over 70 poetry & 150 music examples. Ideal with EGFP.

When We Remember EGFP   *ISBN 9780980351040*
Essential Guide to Funeral Planning
130 page softcover book
Selecting a funeral director, funeral choices
& examples. Ideal companion to CITS.

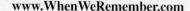

When We Remember CITX   *ISBN 9780980351057*
Condolence Book for Larger Funerals
24 page hardcover book & dust jacket
Perfect addition for CITS condolence register
when extra pages are required.

When We Remember CD   *ISBN 9780980351019*
When We Remember – Music CD
24 Track Music CD
Specially recorded classical, sacred & secular
music perfect for funerals or remembrance.

www.WhenWeRemember.com

 3 thingz

Three Things Publishing
45 Emma Street Mona Vale NSW 2103 Australia   ACN 120839705
Email: info@3thingz.com   Fax: +61 2 99 400 100
Tel: Australia 1800 241 131   World: +61 429 400 100

Abraham, Melissa.
When We Remember: Comfort & Inspiration in Time of Sorrow

4th Edition 2009

Bibliography.
Includes index.
ISBN 978-0-9803510-3-3 (hbk. + CD-ROM).

1. Funeral service – Handbooks, manuals, etc. 2. Death care industry – Planning.
3. Death care industry. I. Title.

265.85

Published by:
Three Things Pty Ltd
45 Emma St, Mona Vale
NSW 2103 Australia

Three Things Pty Ltd

Email: info@3thingz.com

www.WhenWeRemember.com

Cover photograph by Jostein Hauge **www.incredipix.com**
Other photography gratefully received from several private collections, or sourced from
www.bigstockphoto.com and **www.istockphoto.com**
Layout and design by Go Design **www.GoDesign.net.au**

ISBN 978-0-9803510-3-3

9 780980 351033

'When We Remember'
Accompanying CD Playlist

Music for Listening and Reflection

1	The Swan *from Carnival of the Animals*	Saint-Saëns	2.55
2	Sicilienne	Faure	2.16
3	Concerto de Aranjuez	Rodrigo	3.00
4	Sonata "Pathetique" *2nd Movt*	Beethoven	3.22
5	Adagio in G minor	Albinoni	3.20
6	Pavanne	Faure	2.43
7	Prelude No.1	Villa-Lobos	1.58
8	Air *from Suite No.3*	J.S.Bach	4.08
9	Sonata "Moonlight" *1st Movt*	Beethoven	2.58
10	Meditation *from Thais*	Massenet	4.09
11	Pie Jesu *from Requiem*	Faure	2.45
12	Canon	Pachelbel	3.12
13	I Know My Redeemer Liveth *from Messiah*	Handel	2.25
14	Jesu, Joy of Man's Desiring	J.S.Bach	2.44
15	Ave Verum	Mozart	2.35

Music for Singing and Ceremony

16	The Lord is My Shepherd	Psalm 23 / Crimond	2.51
17	Going Home (Christ Gone Before)	Unknown / Dvorak	2.55
18	Abide With Me	Lyte / Monk	3.07
19	Going Home (Live in Me)	Abraham / Dvorak	2.48
20	Amazing Grace (Choir)	Traditional	3.10
21	Amazing Grace (Bagpipe)	Traditional	2.25
22	Last Post	Traditional	1.29
23	Reveille	Traditional	0.27
24	Taps	Traditional	0.48

You will find your 'When We Remember' music CD inside the back cover of this book.

When We Remember
www.3thingz.com
ISBN: 978-0-9803510-1-8